# Fisher-Price™
## LittlePeople™
# WRITING

**For the parents:**

Learning with Fisher-Price™ will help to develop some important skills that your child needs before starting school. Writing is an essential but difficult skill for children to master and is central to much of their school learning experience.

Beginning with simple pencil control activities, children will progress on to tracing letters and writing words. In this way, children will learn gradually, happily and with ever-growing confidence. Start with the fun warm-up exercise and use the reward stickers on the pages and the pull-out chart to help motivate and maintain enthusiasm.

Active learning is promoted in the school curriculum. Children's learning and understanding are improved with the use of real objects and activities, so try to create writing opportunities whenever possible.

Let your child dictate the pace of the work and avoid spending too long on any one page or activity. Offer lots of praise for effort, and most of all, enjoy this special and exciting time!

This book belongs to:

_____

Age:

_____

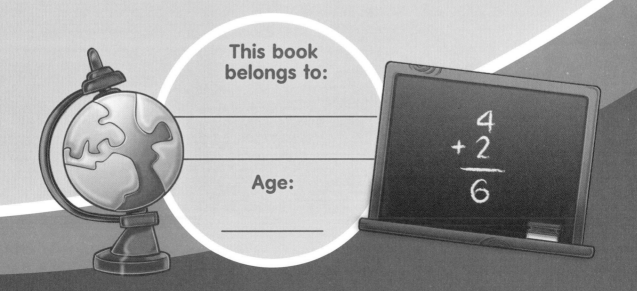

$$\begin{array}{r} 4 \\ +\,2 \\ \hline 6 \end{array}$$

# 1 - 2 - 3 - Warm up!

Join Sarah Lynn, Maggie, Eddie, Sonya Lee and Michael as they warm up and get ready for some fun with writing!

**1** Write your name in the air with your finger!

**2** Spell your name - backwards!

**3** Whisper your second name.

**4** Jump like a kangaroo - as high as you can!

**5** Skip around the room like a rabbit!

Page stickers

Reward chart stickers

ab cd

ef gh

ij kl

yz

uv wx

Writing is FUN

Fisher-Price

**Hop on one foot while patting your head.** 6

**Hop on the other foot while clapping your hands.** 7

9 **Shout the alphabet.**

**Say a word that rhymes with 'write'.** 8

10 **Count down from 10 to 1.**

Well done!
Are you ready?
Are you steady?

**Then let's go!**

# Flower power

**Trace the flower stems.**

Great work!
Don't forget your star!

# Amazing maze

Draw a line to guide Maggie and Michael through the maze.

**START**

**FINISH!**

# Loop the loops

Trace and draw the loops.

Super!

# Twisty turns

Trace and draw the twists and turns.

Add this reward sticker to your chart!

a a a a a

A A A A A

aA

bB

apple

bird

b b b b b

B B B B B

ab

Well done!

c c c c c

C C c c c

cat

dog

cC

dD

d d d d d

D D D D D

c d

ab cd

Add this reward sticker to your chart!

e e e e e

E E E E E

eE

fF

elephant

frog

f f f f f

F F F F F

ef

g g g g g

G G G G G

goat

horse

g G

h H

h h h h h

H H H H H

gh

ef
gh

Add this reward
sticker to your chart!

i i i i i

I I I I I

i I

j J

iguana

jaguar

j j j j j

J J J J J

i j

You are a star!

k k k k k

K K K K K

koala

lion

kK

lL

l l l l l

L L L L L

k l

ijkl

m m m m m

M M M M M

mM

nN

monkey

nose

n n n n n

N N N N N

mn

o o o o o

O O O O O

octopus

penguin

oO

pP

p p p p p

P P P P P

op

mn
op

Add this reward
sticker to your chart!

q q q q q

Q Q Q Q Q

qQ

rR

queen

rhino

r r r r r

R R R R R

qr

Great work!
Don't forget your star!

s s  s s s

S S  S S S

seal

tiger

s S

t T

t t  t t t

T T  T T T

s t

qr
st

Add this reward
sticker to your chart!

u u u u u
U U U U U

uU

vV

umbrella

vulture

v v v v v
V V V V V

uv

Hooray!

W W w w w

W W W W W

x-ray fish

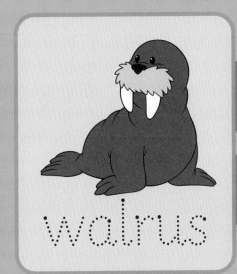

walrus

w W

x X

X X X X X

X X X X X

w x

uv
wx

Add this reward
sticker to your chart!

y y y y y y y

Y Y Y Y Y Y

y Y

z Z

yak

zebra

z z z z z z

Z Z Z Z Z

y z

Good job!

# Words

Look at the colour words and 'things that go'.
Trace the words.

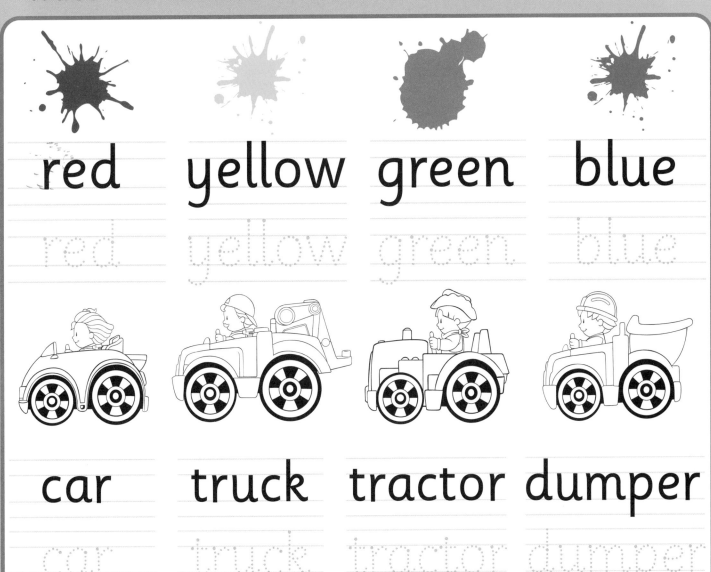

red     yellow     green     blue

~~red~~  ~~yellow~~  ~~green~~  ~~blue~~

car     truck     tractor     dumper

~~car~~  ~~truck~~  ~~tractor~~  ~~dumper~~

yz

# Phrases

Colour the pictures, then write a phrase to describe each one.

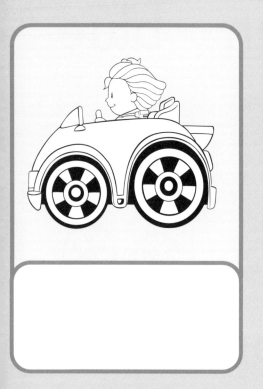

# Super sentences

Try writing a sentence to go with the pictures.

Writing is FUN

Add this reward sticker to your chart!

Name:

Age:

My family:

Favourite thing:

Favourite pet:

Favourite food:

When I grow up I'd like to:

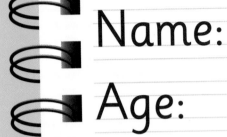